CW00394165

CAT HAIRS

In memory of:
TERRY, DIBBLE, SALLY
& for JIM

# The
# SECRET THOUGHTS
## of
# CATS

a cat.

First published in 1996
This paperback edition published 2001

Copyright Steven Appleby © 1996

The moral right of the author
has been asserted.

Bloomsbury Publishing PLC
38 Soho Square, London W1D 3HB

ISBN 0 7475 5850 7

Printed in Denmark by
Nørhaven Paperback A-S

# Incorporating the INFINITE SUBTLETY of CAT EXPRESSIONS

Steven Appleby

Happy.

Sad.

Mildly
amused.

Pensive.

Waiting to
be fed.

Just been
fed.

Pleased.

Rather
cross.

Utterly
furious.

Slightly
irritated but
concealing it
well.

Staring at a
blank wall.

Sexually
aroused.

Not
interested.

Can't be
bothered.

About to kill
something.

About to do
nothing at all.

Suspicious...

Using the
cat tray.

Being watched
using the
cat tray.

Gloomy.

Bored.

Being
laughed at.

Worrying an
unintelligible
cat worry.

asleep.

As good as
asleep.

Surprised.

Surprised but
pretending
not to be.

Gazing out of
the window.

Seeing something
exciting.

Purring.

Silent.

Not
thinking.

Thinking...

Thinking about
nothing.

Thinking about
bottom licking.

Sitting in a
cardboard box.

About to climb
inside a
carrier-bag.

Watching
invisible things.

Watching you
doing something
personal and
embarrassing.

Wondering if there is a God.

Wondering what
was here before
the universe began.

Suspecting that
humans have
the ability to
read cat-thoughts.

Inscrutable.

Dead.

*Afterthoughts...*

If you put a piece
of paper, however
small, on the floor,
I will sit
on it.

I will touch an
outstretched pencil,
or finger, with
my nose.

My tongue
feels like
Velcro.

I have
unexplained
knobbly lumps
under my fur.

I live in 3 other
houses besides
yours.

I have 3 other names, too.

We cats have
come here to take
over your planet,
earthling.

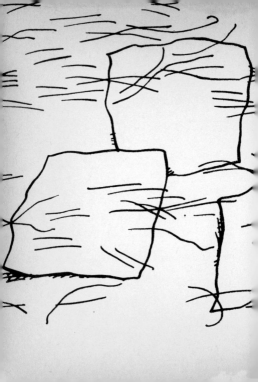

CAT HAIRS
ON CUSHIONS